'fitt for the Manicorde'

A seventeenth-century English collection of keyboard music
58 pieces for harpsichord, clavichord and organ

Edited by
CHRISTOPHER HOGWOOD

68 West End   46 Laurie Crescent
Launton   Henleaze
Bicester   Bristol
Oxon OX26 5DG   BS9 4TA

Contents

Preface

The period of English keyboard music that lies between the death of Thomas Tomkins, the 'last of the virginalists,' in 1656 and the arrival of Handel in London has not until recently attracted much scholarly attention; apart from dutiful surveys of Purcell's keyboard works, there has been less interest in Croft or Blow, little written on Matthew Locke (nothing recent), and almost complete neglect of his 17th-century contemporaries. Yet this was a period of momentous musical as well as political changes; it was during the Commonwealth and Restoration that the seeds of a new style in keyboard music were sown, and the last thirty years of the century show the growth of the new formulas and textures of the keyboard suite that were to dominate the first half of the next century.

Much of the evidence for this development is contained in what are essentially domestic collections – either household manuscripts or the few publications which were aimed at the amateur market. The most complex and carefully presented print, Locke's *Melothesia* (1673), included music by the now little-known Roberts, Preston, Gregory, Thatcher, Hall, Smith and Diessner, and was not a commercial success – the promised sequel was never issued. *Parthenia* had appeared in four editions between 1612/13 and 1655, and three editions of Playford's more trivial anthology of short pieces *Musicks Handmaid*, each larger than the previous one, appeared between 1663 and 1678; the composers included Bryan, Jackson, Lawes, Locke, Mell, Moss, Pratt, Rogers and Sandley – again, not names to conjure with today.

Amongst manuscripts, Elizabeth Rogers' collection of 1656 (Add. 10337) – the last of the virginal books – shows a grouping of dances as embryonic suites together with mixed Anglo/French ornaments very similar to the present MS; composers include Thomas Strengthfeild, La Barre, Mercure as well as earlier repertoire by Gibbons and Byrd's evergreen 'Battaile'; comparable collections are William Ellis' book (Och. 1236, from the 1650s),

'Morgan his Book' (Och. 1003, between 1640 and 1690) and the collection signed 'R. Goodson' (Och. 1177, c.1660–1690). Since multi-composer collections were the norm, Diessner's lost *Kitharapaideia, or a Book of Lessons for the Harpsichords . . . containing a great variety of several Humours, as Preludes, Allemands, Curanto's, Sarabands, Jiggs and Airs*, as announced in *The London Gazette* 27 November 1684, leaves a tantalising hiatus.

Possibly the very domesticity of these collections is responsible for their present neglect, while, conversely, the seriousness of Locke's collection inhibited its popularity in its own day; certainly, the majority of later published keyboard collections from post-Restoration England respected their amateur market and contained only basic instructions on notation, fingering and ornamentation, followed by a graded sequence of short pieces.

The present manuscript, dateable to the 1680s, has been in private hands since it was first noted in the 1950s, and is unusual in its high degree of foreign influence. French *doubles* and airs, music by Lully and La Barre, with fingering notated in a non-English system and a unique mention of the clavichord ('fitt for the Manicorde') all demonstrate a strong foreign interest. First listed by Otto Haas (item 732 in his catalogue 32 [1951]) as a 'Collection of pieces for Spinet & "Manicorde" (Clavichord)', no provenance was given and nothing can now be traced in the firm's records (private communication from Albi Rosenthal). It was bought by Thurston Dart, who published two pieces from it in 1960[1] (and had it rebound in 1963), was again sold (Sotheby's 27 November 1987, Lot 286) and is now in the collection of the present writer (shelf-mark M 1471).

The volume is oblong quarto, 14.5 × 19.5 cm (trimmed), with four pre-ruled six-line staves per page; it was probably supplied by John Playford, who held a virtual monopoly of 'all sorts of Rul'd Paper for Musick, and

Books ready Bound up'.[2] The watermark is of the Dutch Lion type, Heawood nos. 3141–3142 (London c.1685–1700), but made by or for the Dutch from c.1650–1700,[3] and countermarked with a distinctive monogram, possibly to be interpreted as 'VDL' for the Van der Ley family: examples of this countermark in musical sources are entirely in keeping with the 1680s date implied by some of the contents.

The book is copied in brown ink by three professional hands from both ends, the reverse end (pieces **50–53**) begun in an earlier, more old-fashioned Hand A, with more archaic spelling ('Corantt'); this hand recurs on pp. 56–8, but the majority of the volume is in Hand B, imitated in what may be a pupil's hand on p. 51 and a few scribblings elsewhere. A later Hand C fills pp. 44–5, which appear to have been left blank in the original scheme, with piece **23**.

The earliest pagination was from the reverse, pp. 1–74; the folio containing pp. 43 and 44 is missing, but with no apparent excision. No music was copied from this end after p. 67 and these numbers were later cancelled. Present pagination is from 1–181, with 166 accidentally omitted. A folio has also been removed between pp. 114 and 115 but before the earlier pagination was made, and again with no musical hiatus. One, or possibly two folios are missing from the beginning of the book, and one from the reverse end: it is possible they contained music, but from the evidence of other collections, it is more likely to have been explanations of ornaments and fingering, and probably an index, since the manuscript has been twice paginated.

No composers' names are given, and only a minority of the movements have titles, although the missing covers and fly leaves may have contained more information. Concordances so far identified are few, but show an interest in English theatre music, French airs varied in *style brisé* and music with a Royalist flavour (possibly the

---

1 The two 'Allemandes fitt for the Manicorde' in *Clavichord Music of the Seventeenth Century* (ed. Dart) Stainer & Bell Ltd, Reigate (1960), pp. 2–5.

2 Robert Thompson, 'Manuscript Music in Purcell's London', *Early Music* 23 (1995), 605–18.

3 Heawood, 'Papers used in England after 1600 II; c.1680–1750', in *The Library* 11: 4 (March, 1931), p. 484.

taste of a Catholic exile or sympathiser?): the few inscriptions show a Marian leaning, and at least one of the added excercises seems similar to Anglican chant (see Appendix I). Identifications so far proposed include:

1, 2 : similar opening to "When the King enjoys his own again", a popular Royalist song (cf. Thomas Strengthfeild's setting in Elizabeth Rogers' Virginal Book, GB-Lbl Add. 10337, f. 5^v)

6 = "The French Balletto" [anon.] in Elizabeth Rogers' Virginal Book, f. 6 (no. 7), Och. 437, f. 12, "Almayne Gottier[?]" [anon. possibly Gaultier], Lk 46.78/748 Ms. 46.78/748 (Anne Cromwell's Virginal Book) f. 6, "A French Balletto", Lüneburg, Ratsbücherei, KN 146, nos. 483 and 656 ('Allemand' and 'Mascharada') in G, NYp Drexel 5609, p. 41 'Almayne' [anon., in G] and many lute sources, where it is 'Ballet' or 'Balletto'.
Again, a similar opening to "When the King enjoys his own again" (see **1** above).

8 = Och. 1177, 12^v, "Ayre" tentatively attributed to John Roberts by Candace Bailey (*Late-seventeenth-century English Keyboard Music*, A-R Editions, Madison, 1997)

9, 9b = Och. 1177 13^r, untitled, also tentatively attributed to John Roberts (see **8** above)
Och. 1177 integrates the *double* as repeats, not as a separate piece

10, 10b = La Barre. Concordances include:
Paris BN Rés. 1184–5 (Cosyn) p. 174 "Coranto . . . Mr. Tresure" with variation
Och. 1236, p. 10 "Corant. Labar" with variation
NYp Drexel 5611 (Heardson), p. 78 (Gibbons)
Och. 1236, p. 3 (Tresure)
Berlin, Lynar A-1, pp. 298–9 "Courante de La Barre . . . Variatio"
Chigi Q IV 24, ff. 47^r–47^v "Corente di Monsu della Bara"
NL -Uim q-1, (Gresse), f. 14^r "Courante"

15: incipit similar to Courante in Lüneburg, Ratsbücherei, Mus. ant. pract. 1198, p. 56 (anon,, G minor)
Also related to Lawes "The Kings Coranto" (*Courtly Masquing Ayres*, no. 6 in G minor) which in turn shares five bars with a Courant by Chambonnieres (Book. 1, Paris, 1670)

23 = Lully, Chorus: 'La beauté la plus sévère' (*Atys*, 1676), LWV 53/75. The form is curiously distorted in this transcription by a two-beat extension of bar 13. Other keyboard concordances include:
F-Pn: Vm7-6307-1, pp. 16–17 [no. 10] ('La beaute la plus seuere')
F-Psg: Gen-2356, no. 17 ('Gauotte')
S-L: Lund-24, ff. 89^v–90^r ('La bonté') in A
S-SK: Skara-493a, f. 93^v ('La Beautee') in A

S-Skma; Tabulatur no. 7, ff. 2^v–3^r ('La Beaute')

28 from Thomas Farmer, *A Consort of Musick in four parts containing 33 Lessons beginning with an Ouverture* (1686) [BL K.7.c.4 missing the viola part-book]; a MS copy dated 9 June 1691 is in the three-part BL Add. MSS 29283-5, Thomas Fuller's part-books, dated 1682 (pp. 165–6 in Violin 1). See Appendix II for a transcription of the printed source.[4]

The likeliest candidate for the Organist of Chichester who requested the setting is Samuel Pearson (or Peirson) who served from 1677–1720 and appears to have been a non-juror: in January 1711 he was suspended for three months for having declared that "the late King William [III] was a pickpocket; that he had seen the king at his Chapel and he had no more religion than a dog".[5]

33 printed in *Musicks Hand-maid* (1663) p. 27 as "Coranto la Chabotte" (anon., in D). Also found in:
F-Psg MS 2350, ff. 8^v–9^r untitled, anon. (in C)
D-Kk Ms 376 ff. 22^v–23^r "Courante la Chabotte" (anon., in C)
Stockholm, Riksarkivet; *Handlingar rörande teatern. 1: 1624–1782*, 'Courante la Chavotte' (anon., in C)
Örebro, Karolinska Skolan; uncatalogued MS, ff. 1^v–2 'Courant . . . neuer Gavotto' (anon., in C)

38, 38b = La Barre. Concordances include:
Och. 1236, pp. 11–12 "Courant" with variation
NYp Drexel 5611 (Heardson), p. 103 (no. 64) "Corant Labar" with variation

56 this ground bass, and the equally unusual bass on p. 13 (see Appendix I, Example 1) are both found in two sources associated with the Jesuit musician Anthony Poole, who died in 1692. GB-Ob Mus. Sch. C71 contains divisions for solo bass viol, and F-Pn Vm7 137323 and 137317 contain alternative versions for viol with accompaniment; the titles are 'Chacone' and 'Chacona' and both are in the same keys as found in this MS.[6]

The very first pieces in the collection set out the French credentials of the volume – two closely related demonstrations of variation techniques, followed by three (related) numbers that demonstrate variation of setting and tempo (triple and 'fast'), after which organised suite movements follow – a plan very similar to that of *Melothesia* and other didactic collections. Metrical notations of 'free' preludes are included (as was also attempted in *Melo-*

thesia)[7] and echoes of the Italian toccata style and 'Mr Matteis' Trumpet' (*Senr. Nicola's Trumpet*, Add. 22099, f. 14) contribute to the final 'voluntaries'.

Original titles are given in full; spellings vary, with 'Allemande' but also 'Alman'; 'Eare' for 'Air' suggests a northern or Scottish dialect, and the scribe was uncertain of some dance types ('Eare or Courante', **33** and 'Eare or Allemande', **47**). The first titled number (**13**) introduces a completely titled French suite of *Prelude – Allemande – Courante – Sarabande* (plus *Variation*).

All editorial suggestions are in square brackets. Dart identified **3** as a 'corant', and **4** a 'sarabande', although they appear to be *contrafacta*; **5** might also be construed as another variant, with unchanging harmony, all three being didactic examples. The suggestion of 'Jig-Almaine' for **7** is adopted from *Melothesia* (it is possible that the whole piece is to be played in compound triple rhythm; see below). In France gigues were often indistinguishable from allemandes (see lute collections such as *La Rhétorique des Dieux*) and in the Bauyn MS two allemandes by J. C. de la Barre are each repeated *verbatim*, with the title changed to 'Gigue'; in England Benjamin Rogers has a gigue notated in almain rhythm (Och. 1236 ff. 41^v–42) and other jig-almains are found from Albertus Bryne in Bod. Ms. Mus.Sch. D. 219 and Och. 1177 and by Moss in *Melothesia*.

The collection appears to contain no sarabandes with the typical opening pattern of three repeated notes, except that **36**, in spite of its title ('A litle courant') would seem to have the opening phraseology and style of a sarabande (and is also melodically related to the preceding Courant); this is probably another example of scribal confusion. The rondo form of **51**, which might be a hornpipe or Round O or jig (as *Melothesia* no. 16) is unusual in being in four sections with section 1 repeated an octave higher as section 3.

Neither of the Bible verses that introduce **57** and **58** appears to be taken *verbatim* from existing OT translations

4 This identification was kindly provided by Peter Holman.
5 See Watkins Shaw *The Succession of Organists* , Oxford (1999), p. 77.
6 Information supplied by François-Pierre Goy.

7 See C. Bailey, 'Préludes non mesurés en Angleterre' in *Revue de musicologie* 87 no. 2 (2001), p. 289.

(Tyndale, Coverdale, Common Prayer 1599, Breeches Bible 1603), but are closest to the readings of the Reims Douai translation, printed in 1609. It also seems odd that a keyboard composer would not prefer the reference to 'virginalls and organs' of the 1599 and 1603 translations, rather than 'strings and Organs'.

Evidence that the collection was copied in a planned sequence comes from the correction given in the titles of **44** and **45** ('A short Eare in way of a Prelude, to be play'd before the other Eare'), the two full suites **13–16b** and **17–21** (though not so titled), and other, less extended, grouping by keys which is apparent, despite dances added later sometimes breaking the intended sequence. The identification of groupings as suites in the index to this edition is editorial; although in some cases it may seem over-optimistic, it is useful on two counts: firstly, to point up deliberate sequences in a single tonality and to distinguish these from pieces which appear to be primarily progressive didactic examples (**1** and **2**, **3–5**), and others in a random succession of keys; secondly, to encourage the player to expand these embryonic suites with pieces from elsewhere in the collection, or even from other sources; suites by a single composer were not the norm (Purcell's posthumous *Choice Collection* was the first exception). B minor is the most remote key represented (a rare tonality, though favoured by Draghi), and seems to be required by a sequence of rising pitches: **44** to **51** move through A, B, C and D.

Variations on a ground bass were a popular feature of this period, and La Folia occurs with depressing frequency in 17th and early 18th-century MSS. This collection also includes a Bergamask, plus sketches and bass-lines which suggest that such basic patterns were used for teaching purposes (see Appendix I).

All the movements with variations are in Hand B with more courants having *doubles* than any other dance form. Because of page turns, the variations cannot easily have been intended for *alternatim* playing; however, **9** and **9b** as preserved in Och. 1177 have their variations

interpolated, and where possible such pairs are grouped together on an opening in this edition to allow the modern player the option.

In addition to the Overture, the two Allemandes for the clavichord, and the Lully Gavotte (**23**), other pieces may well be arrangements. Those with running thirds and sixths (e.g. **27**, **34**, **35b**) or with imitation between inner parts suggest a consort original, as do those with particularly high or low tessitura.

Some of the short scribblings and exercises may be related to the pieces they follow in this teaching collection; they are all in Hand B (or the amateur hand) and are transcribed in Appendix I. The figured basses on pp. 33 and 64 (also in Appendix I) are the same sequence in different notation.

The music is notated on a six-line stave throughout, in C, G and F clefs; G4 is used once (probably to correct a miscopying by a third) in **55**, b. 250, and music for each hand is kept to its own stave, in normal 17th-century style. The beaming and tied notes of the original are preserved; sometimes a tie is the result of a line-break, but often, as Playford observed in *Musicks Hand-maid* 'many *Quavers* and *Semiquavers* are tyed together by a Dash continued quite thorough them; but it is done only for conveniency and benefit of the sight, and makes no alteration in the Time'. In **57** and **58** a tie is doubled, and a single slur over more than two notes, as in **55** and **43**, bar 17, presumably indicates a continuous tie. This edition retains these nuances, since tied notes in general may be reiterated depending on the type of instrument being played. Similarly, the variant beaming of groups of notes can illuminate phrasing, fingering and articulation.

Accidentals and key-signatures are treated often freely and modally; the Prelude, for example, of the D minor suite (**13–16b**) is given with one flat, the remainder without key signature, while C minor (**42**, **43**) is indicated with two flats. The natural sign is not used, and accidentals are mostly (but not uniformly) assumed to last for one

note only; editorial additions proposed here in brackets aim to intrude as little as possible, though a player can make more dramatic decisions.

As with the repertoire, so the ornaments also show a mix of new French and old Anglo-Dutch style. Five established symbols are listed by Locke in 1673, and others can be found in sources by Prencourt, Blakeston (Add. 17853, dated 1694), Robert Carr (1684) and Purcell together with their suggested realisations.

Table of ornaments

Forefall		
Backfall	or	
Shake		
Plain Note and Shake		
Beat		
Slide (or Slur)		
Battery		

In French music, however, ⟿ signified a shake or *tremblement*, and the *port de voix*, variously marked as ⸌ or ⸌ indicated upper or lower appoggiature; the simple *pincé* = had no equivalent in 17th-century England, since, as Purcell noted, 'you allwayes shake from the note above and beat from the note or half note below'.

The positioning of double-stroke ornaments varies, sometimes above the note, other times through the tail; such differences are preserved here and may be meaningful.[8] It is questionable whether there is a difference between a double-stroke and French shake within same piece (**46**) or even on the same note (**53**, b. 4); this last

8 See John Harley 'Ornaments in English Keyboard Music of the Seventeenth and Eighteenth Centuries', *Music Review* 31 (1970), pp. 178–84.

may be an alternative or a second thought, as also the combination of 'chute' plus shake in **16**, b. 11. The double-stroke often appears to be used where a French source would have a *pincé* and such an ornament when fingered with '4' (in **52**) certainly suggests a lower auxiliary.

Compound ornaments are created in some numbers: the backfall and shake, for example, in **11**, bb. 7 and 20, **51**, b. 16 and **52**, b. 10, while the slurred note before a double-stroke shake in **18** and **22** presumably prevents the normal repetition of the upper note.

The indication for the broken chord or 'battery' although interpreted in most English publications as an upwards spread, may also have been executed in the French manner, with passing notes as suggested by D'Anglebert (1689)

or even as a reiterated arpeggiation, as Prencourt suggests:

This latter suggestion might be useful in **58**, bb. 27 onwards.

The slide is written out in full in **53** and the only occurrence of single-stroke ornaments (in **58**, b. 158) is possibly an error (as in Elizabeth Rogers' Virginal Book) or may be another indication of a slide.

Simultaneous ornaments in lh and rh occur in **49**, b. 16, **55**, b. 56, **42**, bb. 10, 17, 21 and 24, **46**, b. 13, and in **50**, b. 20 the ornament is marked twice on same note. Doubled ornaments – double-stroke and French trill – are found in **53**, b. 4, and several bars in **42** employ two different shakes simultaneously. Trills are written out in full in **58**, as in earlier virginalists' style; of the left-hand trills Roger North wrote that 'It is the common practise of organists, instead of the grace they call the beat-up, upon the low keys, to put downe two to sound together in semitone, which in the same designe, hath a better effect'.

In **51** and elsewhere the backfall/forefall distinction sometimes seems blurred; certainly the final bars of each section of **51** seem to require an ornament from below,

rather than above. The ∧ ornament in **13**, b. 3 cannot be identified, though possibly a backfall + forefall, a sort of turn, is intended; its only other appearance is later in Hotteterre where it represents a 'coulement' or upper appoggiatura. Chromatic inflection is never indicated since it is assumed all ornaments will be played within the prevailing tonality (e.g. in **28**, b. 62 the shake will be with A flat).

A double bar in a dance movement, Purcell explains, 'imports ye must play ye Strain twice' and is interpreted here as a repeat mark. In pieces of more than two sections (such as the Bergamask and Folia variations) such repeats may be optional; unlike the majority of Airs, **49** is divided into four parts, but only two of the divisions imply repeats. A *petite reprise* is indicated in **52** (i.e. both sections repeated in full *plus* the *petite reprise*), and written out (with slightly varied harmony) in **33**. This formula can be utilized in other dance movements according to taste.

The original notation of final bars in bipartite pieces has been preserved, but sometimes needs adapting either for upbeats or to improve a transition; solutions include omitting a link the second time (**3**, lh, b. 16), missing out a note that will conflict with the upbeat first time (**1**, lh, b. 4), or even adding an extra cadential bar (as demonstrated by comparing the original texts of **9** and **9b**). Note-values of chords in cadential bars are sometimes arbitrary and can vary between rh and lh depending on the anticipated upbeat, but since the intention is always clear they have not been editorially improved here. Very rarely first- and second-time bars are notated with exceptional accuracy: see **14**, bars 8 and 16.

The conventional left-hand cadential pattern such as **1**, b. 4 is sometimes notated with the lowest note held (see **2**), which may be an alternative over-legato interpretation. In general arpeggiated cadential chords may be improved with ties, and indeed throughout those pieces that utilize *brisure* an over-legato would be appropriate. An alternative source for **9** (Och. 1177), for example, gives slurs (indicating tenuto) over much of the quaver figura-

tion, just as other versions of **6** indicate a more filled-out left hand part, which players may adopt to taste. Editorial filling is added here only when there is a troubling harmonic hiatus or ambiguity.

More than half the pieces in this manuscript are methodically fingered, making it one of the most instructive 17th-century sources for English technique. However, the system used, with × (thumb)-1-2-3-4, is more typical of Italian notation than English or French, and is not shared with any other English writer other than Prencourt, who used thumb-1-2-3-4. (Roger North, *Plaine & Easie Rules c.*1700). The numbering, modernized here, gives us important information on touch, articulation, ornamentation, tempo and chord playing, providing some caution is observed; occasionally fingering was marked *before* inner parts were added (see **2b**, bb. 4 and 8), or in other pieces before an ornament was added (**36b**); in a few cases it is simply impossible (**35b**, b. 16, lh; see Textual Notes). Nevertheless, some general rules can be deduced: reiteration of a note is made with a change of finger; changing a finger on a held note ('organists' fingering') is expected (**1b**, b. 8); the thumb is frequently used on a short key (**26b**, rh bb. 19 and 25), and also for long sequences of inner part writing (**45b**, bb. 10–11); in sequences of sixths and thirds (**35b**) a relatively 'modern' fingering is used to give legato outer parts, while at other times extended sequences using the same finger are allowed.

Only one piece in the collection has a tempo mark ('Fast' for **5**), but for many dances the time-signature would have constituted a speed indication; Purcell's *Choice Collection of Lessons* (1696) explains the three markings – 𝄴, 𝄵, ⊘ – as 'ye first is a very slow movement, ye next a little faster, and ye last a brisk & airy time, & each of them has allways to ye length of one Semibreif in a barr, which is to be held in playing as long as you can moderately tell four; by saying one, two, three, four'. Other contemporary writers agree that ⊘ indicates 'Brisk and light Ayres' and 'as fast as the regular motions of a *Watch*' (i.e. ♩ = MM 120).

For triple time Playford in 1694 noted $\frac{3}{2}$ as the slowest, 3 or 3ı as faster, and $\frac{3}{8}$ which is performed 'as fast again'. The 1696 *Choice Collection* adds a further distinction, that 3ı 'has three Crotchets in a barr, and they are to be play'd slow', while plain 3 'has ye same as ye former but is play'd faster'. Triple time was slowest in the sarabande, which had started as a fast dance but by the end of the 17th-century could be described by Dean Aldrich as 'a soft passionate Mvt always set in a slow Triple' (Och. MS 1187, c.1695). The triple section of the Farmer overture (**28**, b. 22) is also, somewhat surprisingly, marked 'slow time' in the original consort version.

In those movements with variations, the elaboration of the *double* will suggest a moderate tempo, particularly in Almands. No distinction of tempo seems implied by the French title Allemande (eight pieces so named, plus one 'Eare or Allemande') rather than the single English Almand (**27**). The two final voluntaries probably require differing tempi for contrasting sections, and even *senza misura* in the manner of an Italian toccata.

The 'tempering' of dotted rhythms was an important aspect of performance style, either with 'double dotting' (a modern term) or *notes inégales*, as well as the shortening of up-beats and notes after rests. A note of caution, however, is sounded by **27** where the uniform dotted pattern implied after rests is *not* adopted even when it could be notated (b. 20). The unusual rhythmic variety of **7** [Jigg-Almaine] suggests assimilating the triplets or even adapting the metre of the whole piece to compound time. Two differing contemporary notations for a Froberger Gigue provide a model for this:

By analogy, the opening of **7** would be played:

Playford lists instruments appropriate to this repertoire: 'The *Virginal* is strung with one single Course of Strings; the *Harpsichord* with two or more, and is fuller and lowder; and the *Organ* is framed to contain [a] variety of Sets or Stops of pipes'. He illustrates a short-octave keyboard with bottom note C, but notes that this compass of '29 Keys' was 'according to the ancient Standard . . . but of later times they add to that number both above and below'. This collection calls for bottom G once (**22**) and bottom A several times (**14, 16, 16b, 53**); in *Melothesia* we find low B (used by Preston), low A (Preston, Moss, Thatcher, Locke) and bottom G (Diessner), possible indicators that certain composers preferred specific ranges. The two 'voluntaries' (**57, 58**) although appearing similar to organ pieces of this period, are not written for a divided stop (both low and high sections over-ride the possible division of a register), and, with a few exceptions, hand-collisions are specifically avoided, indicating a single manual instrument.

The 'Clarichord, or Manichord' according to Grassineau's dictionary of 1740 'cannot be heard at any considerable distance; hence some call it the dumb Spinet'. From title-pages of both French (Attaingnant's *Quatorze Gaillardes . . . en la tabulature du jeu d'Orgues Espinettes Manicordions . . .* 1531) and Italian collections (Gardano's *Intabolatura nova . . . da sonare per arpichordi, Claviciembali, Spinette, & Manachordi . . .* 1551) the term had been internationally known for more than a century. But the two Allemandes 'fitt [i.e. arranged] for the Manicorde' are the only pieces of English origin to specify this instrument. The suggestion that the collection might be considered clavichord music is supported by the only specified dynamic change, the 'eccho' markings in **40**. Such instructions are rare but not unknown in English keyboard music (a movement by John Roberts (Almain) in Drexel 5611 has a passage marked 'softly'), but the writing in this instance (bb. 25–6) precludes a change of manual if the parts are to be sustained as written, assuming that the 'eccho' applies to both staves; a clavichord would therefore be the only instrument capable of executing this nuance literally.

Acknowledgements

Thanks are due to Robert Rawson, Curtis Lasell, Prof. Eamon Duffy, Robert Thompson, the late Robert Spencer, Peter Holman, Bruce Gustafson, François-Pierre Goy, Derek Adlam, Heather Jarman, David Chung and Per Hartmann for their varied assistance in this edition.

Bibliography

Candace Bailey: *English Keyboard Music c.1625–1680* (PhD diss.: Duke University, 1989)

John Caldwell: *English Keyboard Music before the Nineteenth Century* (Blackwell, Oxford, 1973)

Barry Cooper: *English Solo Keyboard Music of the Middle and Late Baroque* (Garland, New York, 1989)

Bruce Gustafson and R. Peter Wolf, eds: *Harpsichord Music Associated with the Name of La Barre* (Broude Trust, New York, 1999).

John Harley: *British Harpsichord Music* (Scolar Press, Aldershot, 1992–4)

J. Brian Hodge: *English Harpsichord Repertoire, 1660–1714.* (PhD diss.: University of Manchester, 1989)

Matthew Locke (ed. Hogwood): *Melothesia* (OUP, 1987)

Roger North (ed. Wilson): *On Music; Being a Selection from his Essays, Written during the Years c.1695–1728* (Novello, London, 1959)

Christopher Hogwood
Cambridge, June 2003
hogwood@hogwood.org

Vorwort

Englischer Tastenmusik aus der Zeit zwischen dem Tod von Thomas Tomkins in 1656, dem «letzten der Virginalkomponisten», und der Ankunft Händels in London wurde bis vor kurzem wenig Aufmerksamkeit geschenkt. Abgesehen von obligatorischen Schriften zu Purcells Tastenmusik gibt es kaum Interesse an Croft, oder Blow, es gibt wenig über Matthew Locke (nichts in den letzten Jahren), und seine Zeitgenossen aus dem 17. Jh. werden fast alle ignoriert. Und dennoch war das eine Epoche von enormen musikalischen wie politischen Umwälzungen: die Anfänge eines neuen Stils für Tastenmusik fallen in die Zeit der Restauration, und das letzte Drittel des Jahrhunderts sorgt für die Entwicklung jener neuen formelhaften Wendungen und Strukturen der Suiten für Tasteninstrumente, die die erste Hälfte des folgenden Jahrhunderts bestimmen sollten.

Das meiste überlieferte Material für diese Entwicklung gehört zu Hausmusik-Sammlungen – es handelt sich entweder um Manuskripte, von denen im engsten privaten Kreis gespielt wurde oder um einige wenige Veröffentlichungen, die für den Liebhabergebrauch bestimmt waren. Die komplizierteste und am sorgfältigsten ausgeführte Publikation ist Lockes *Melothesia* (1673); darin enthalten ist Musik von den heute unbekannten Komponisten Roberts, Preston, Gregory, Thatcher, Hall, Smith und Diessner; sie war kein kommerzieller Erfolg – eine angekündigte Folge kam nie zustande. Zwischen 1612/13 und 1655 waren vier Ausgaben von *Parthenia* erschienen, und zwischen 1663 und 1678 drei Ausgaben von Playfords relativ trivialer Anthologie kurzer Stücke – *Musicks Handmaid,* eine größer als die andere; darin finden sich Komponisten wie Bryan, Jackson, Lawes, Locke, Mell, Moss, Pratt, Rogers und Sandley – alles Namen, die heute vergessen sind.

Unter all den Manuskripten gibt es in Elizabeth Rogers' Sammlung von 1656 (Add. 10337) – die letzten Virginalienbücher – eine Gruppierung von Tänzen als Suiten im Anfangsstadium gemeinsam mit gemischten anglo/

französischen Verzierungen, die mit der vorliegenden Quelle große Ähnlichkeit aufweisen. Darin sind Komponisten wie Thomas Strengthfeild, La Barre und Mercure vertreten sowie ein früheres Repertoire mit Gibbons und Byrds Schlager «Battaille». Vergleichbare Sammlungen sind das Buch von William Ellis (Och. 1236, aus den 1650er), «Morgan his Book» (Och. 1003, zwischen 1640 und 1690) und die Sammlung signiert «R. Goodson» (Och. 1177, ca. 1660–1690). Da Sammlungen, mehreren Komponisten gewidmet, die Norm zu jener Zeit waren, hinterlässt Diessners verlorene *Kitharapaideia, oder ein Übungsbuch für das Cembalo . . . mit vielen verschiedenen Launen, wie Präludien, Allemanden, Curanto's, Sarabanden, Jiggs und Airs,* angekündigt in *The London Gazette* vom 27. November 1684, eine verlockende Lücke.

Wahrscheinlich ist es der Hausmusikcharakter, der diese Sammlungen in Vergessenheit geraten ließ; andrerseits verhinderte jedoch gerade die Ernsthaftigkeit der Lockeschen Sammlung bei den Zeitgenossen größere Beliebtheit. Fest steht, dass die Mehrzahl von späteren Ausgaben englischer Tastenmusik nach der Restaurationszeit Rücksicht auf die versierten Dilettanten nahmen und nur die nötigsten Anweisungen in Bezug auf Notation, Fingersatz und Verzierungen geben, gefolgt von gradierten, kurzen Stücken.

Die vorliegende Quelle, aus den 1680er Jahren befindet sich seit ihrer Wiederentdeckung in den 1950er Jahren in Privatbesitz und weist einen ungewöhnlich hohen Grad an fremden Einflüssen auf. Französische *doubles* und *airs*, Musik von Lully und La Barre mit Fingersätzen, die nicht dem englischen System entsprechen, sowie eine einzigartige Erwähnung des Clavichords («fitt for the Manicorde») deuten alle auf starken fremden Einfluss. Erstmalig erwähnt bei Otto Haas (Nummer 732 in seinem Katalog 32 [1951]) als «Sammlung von Stücken für Spinet & „Manicorde" (Clavichord)», ohne Ursprungsbezeichnung, kann man heute nichts mehr im Archiv des Verlags darüber finden (persönliche Mitteilung von Albi Rosenthal). Das Manuskript wurde von Thurston Dart

gekauft, der 1960 zwei Stücke davon verlegte[1] (und es 1963 neu binden ließ), bei Sothebys (am 27. 11. 1987, Artikel 286) wieder verkauft und befindet sich derzeit in der Sammlung des Autors (Signatur M 1471).

Der Band ist im Querformat, 14.5 × 19.5 cm (beschnitten) mit vier vorgezeichneten, sechs-linigen Notensystemen pro Seite. Wahrscheinlich wurde er von John Playford angefertigt, der praktisch ein Monopol für «alle Arten liniertes Papier für Musik, und gebundene Bücher» hatte.[2] Das Wasserzeichen ist dasjenige des holländischen Löwentypus, Heawood Nr. 3141–3142 (London ca. 1685–1700), jedoch für oder von den Holländern zwischen ca. 1650 und 1700 angefertigt;[3] gegengezeichnet ist es mit einem ausgeprägten Monogramm, das vielleicht als VDL, für die Van der Ley Familie, stehen könnte: Beispiele dieser Gegenzeichnung in anderen Musikquellen stimmen mit dem Datum der 1680er Jahre überein, das in einigen der Inhalte angedeutet wird.

Der Band ist in brauner Tinte von drei Berufskopisten geschrieben, und zwar gleichzeitig von vorne und von hinten angefangen. Der hinten begonnene Teil ist älter (Stücke **50–53**) und zeigt die altmodischere Hand des Kopisten A mit altertümlicher Rechtschreibung («Corrant»); dieser Kopist A schrieb auch die Seiten 56–58, jedoch die Mehrheit des Bandes wurde vom Kopisten B ausgeführt (mit einigen Imitationen auf S. 51 (von einem Schüler?) und ein paar Kritzeleien anderswo). Kopist C schrieb das Stück **23** auf den Seiten 44–45, die im Original scheinbar leer gelassen waren.

Die früheste Seitenbezifferung beginnt von hinten, S. 1–74; das Blatt mit S. 43 und 44 fehlt, allerdings ohne merkbare Bruchstellen. Nach S. 67 wurde keine Musik mehr von hinten kopiert, und diese Bezifferungen wurden später annulliert. Die gegenwärtige Seitenbezifferung geht von 1–181, wobei 166 versehentlich ausgelassen ist. Ein

1 Die zwei 'Allemandes fitt for the Manicorde' in *Clavichord Music of the Seventeenth Century* (Hg. Dart) Stainer & Bell Ltd, Reigate (1960), S. 2–5.
2 Robert Thompson, 'Manuscript Music in Purcell's London', *Early Music* 23 (1995), S. 605–618.
3 Heawood, 'Papers used in England after 1600 II; c.1680–1750', in *The Library* 11: 4 (März, 1931), S. 484.

Blatt wurde zwischen 114 und 115 herausgenommen, jedoch schon vor der letzten Bezifferung und daher ohne musikalische Konsequenzen. Ein Blatt, oder sogar zwei, fehlen vom Anfang des Buches und eines vom hinteren Ende: vielleicht enthielten sie Musik, aber zufolge der übrigen Anhaltspunkte aus der Sammlung waren es wahrscheinlich nur Erklärungen von Verzierungen und Fingersätzen, vielleicht auch ein Index, da die Seiten des Manuskripts zweimal beziffert worden waren.

Es gibt keinen Komponistennamen und nur eine geringe Anzahl von Sätzen weist Titeln auf, obwohl die verlorenen Deckblätter und Umschläge eventuell mehr Einzelheiten aufwiesen. Bislang konnten nur wenig Konkordanzen gefunden werden, und diese bekunden Interesse an englischer Theatermusik, französischen *airs* variiert im *style brisé* und königstreu angehauchter Musik (der Geschmack von Katholiken im Exil oder Sympathisanten?): die spärlichen Inschriften lassen Zeichen von Marienverehrung erkennen, und mindestens eine der zugefügten Übungen scheint dem anglikanischen Gesang ähnlich (siehe Anhang I).

Die soweit vorgeschlagenen Identifikationen sind:

1, 2: ähnlicher Anfang «When the King enjoys his own again», ein populäres königstreues Lied (vgl. Thomas Strengthfeilds Satz in *Elizabeth Rogers' Virginal Book*, GB-Lbl Add. 10337, Bl. 5ʳ)

6 = «The French Balletto» [Anon.] in *Elizabeth Rogers' Viriginal Book*, Bl. 6 (Nr. 7), Och. 437, Bl. 12, «Almayne Gottier[?]» [Anon. möglicherweise Gaultier], Lk 46.78/748 Ms. 46.78/748 (*Anne Cromwell's Virginal Book*) Bl. 6, «A French Balletto», Lüneburg, Ratsbücherei, KN 146, Nr. 483 und 656 («Allemand» und «Mascharada») in G, NYp Drexel 5609, S. 41 «Almayne» [Anon., in G] und viele Lautenquellen, in denen es als «Ballet» oder «Balletto» auftritt.
Wieder ein ähnlicher Anfang «When the King enjoys his own again» (siehe **1** oben).

8 = Och. 1177, 12ᵛ, «Ayre» einstweilen John Roberts von Candace Bailey zugeordnet (*Late-seventeenth-century English Keyboard Music*, A-R Editions, Madison, 1997)

9, 9b = Och. 1177 13ʳ, kein Titel, einstweilen auch John Roberts zugeordnet (siehe **8** oben)
Och. 1177 integriert das *double* als Wiederholungen, nicht als eigenständiges Stück

10, 10b = La Barre. Die Konkordanzen sind u.a.:
Paris BN Rés. 1184–5 (Cosyn) S. 174 «Coranto . . . Mr. Tresure» mit Variation
Och. 1236, S. 10 «Corant. Labar» mit Variation
NYp Drexel 5611 (Heardson), S. 78 (Gibbons)
Och. 1236, S. 3 (Tresure)
Berlin, Lynar A–1, S. 298–299 «Courante de La Barre . . . Variatio»
Chigi Q IV 24, Bl. 47ʳ–47ᵛ «Corente di Monsu della Bara»
NL-Uim q–1, (Gresse), Bl. 14ʳ «Courante»

15: Incipit ähnlich der Courante in Lüneburg, Ratsbücherei, Mus. ant. pract. 1198, S. 56 (Anon., G Moll)
Auch mit Lawes «The Kings Coranto» (*Courtly Masquing Ayres*, Nr. 6 in G Moll) verwandt, der wieder fünf Takte mit einem Courant von Chambonnieres teilt (1. Buch, Paris, 1670)

23 = Lully, Chorus: «La beauté la plus sévère» (*Atys*, 1676), LWV 53/75. Die Form dieser Transkription ist merkwürdig verunstaltet von einer Zwei-Takt-Verlängerung von Takt 13.
Andere Tasteninstrument Konkordanzen enthalten:
F-Pn: Vm7–6307–1, S. 16–17 [Nr. 10] («La beaute la plus seuere»)
F-Psg: Gen–2356, Nr. 17 («Gauotte»)
S-L: Lund–24, Bl. 89ᵛ–90ʳ («La bonté») in A
S-SK: Skara–493a, Bl. 93ᵛ («La Beautee») in A
S-Skma; Tabulatur Nr. 7, Bl. 2ᵛ–3ʳ («La Beaute»)

28 aus Thomas Farmer, *A Consort of Musick in four parts containing 33 Lessons beginning with an Ouverture* (1686) [BL K.7.c.4 Viola Stimmenbuch fehlt]; eine Manuskriptkopie datiert 9. Juni 1691 ist in den dreiteiligen Stimmenbüchern Thomas Fullers BL Add. MSS 29283-5, datiert 1682 (S. 165–166 in der 1. Violine). Eine Transkription der gedruckten Quelle ist im Anhang II gegeben.[4]
Der wahrscheinlichste Kandidat für den Organisten von Chichester, der den Satz bestellt hat, ist Samuel Pearson (oder Peirson) der von 1677–1720 gedient hat; er scheint als Geschworener disqualifiziert gewesen zu sein. Im Januar 1711 wurde er drei Monate lang suspendiert, weil er angab, dass «der verstorbene König William [III] ein Taschendieb war; dass er den König in seiner Kapelle gesehen hatte und dass er so religiös wie ein Hund war.»[5]

33 veröffentlicht in *Musicks Hand-maid* (1663) S. 27 als «Coranto la Chabotte» (Anon., in D). Ebenfalls in:
F-Psg MS 2350, Bl. 8ᵛ–9ʳ kein Titel und Anon. (in C)
D-Kk Ms 376 Bl. 22ᵛ–23ᵛ «Courante la Chabotte» (Anon., in C)
Stockholm, Riksarkivet; *Handlingar rörande teatern. 1: 1624–*

1782, «Courante la Chavotte» (Anon., in C)
Örebro, Karolinska Skolan; nicht katalogisiert MS, Bl. 1ᵛ–2 «Courant . . . neuer Gavotto» (Anon., in C)

38, 38b = La Barre. Weitere Konkordanzen u.a.:
Och. 1236, S. 11–12 'Courant' mit Variation
NYp Drexel 5611 (Heardson), S. 103 (Nr. 64) «Corant Labar» mit Variation

56 Dieser *Basso ostinato* sowie der ebenso ungewöhnliche Bass auf S. 13 (siehe Anhang I, 1. Beispiel) finden sich beide in zwei Quellen, die mit dem Jesuitenmusiker Anthony Poole († 1692) in Verbindung gebracht werden. GB-Ob Mus. Sch. C71 enthält Teile für solo Bass Viol, und F-Pn Vm7 137323 und 137317 enthalten alternative Versionen für Viol mit Begleitung; sie sind mit «Chacone» und «Chacona» betitelt und beide sind in der gleichen Tonart, die sich im vorliegenden Manuskript finden.[6]

Die allerersten Werke in der Sammlung legen den französischen Einfluss des Bandes dar – zwei eng verwandte Demonstrationen von Variationstechniken gefolgt von drei (verwandten) Stücken, die Variationen von Satz und Tempo (Dreiertakt und «schnell») aufzeigen; danach kommen strukturierte Suite-Sätze – ein Schema, das dem von *Melothesia* und anderen didaktischen Sammlungen sehr ähnlich ist. Es gibt darin metrische Betonungen von «freien» Präludien (wie in *Melothesia* versucht worden war),[7] und Anklänge an den italienischen Toccatastil und «Mr Matteis' Trumpet» (*Senr. Nicola's Trumpet*, Add. 22099, Blatt 14) sind Teile der letzten Orgelsoli.

Originaltitel werden ganz wiedergegeben, die Rechtschreibung ist unterschiedlich – «Allemande» oder auch «Alman»; «Eare» für «Air» deutet auf einen nördlichen oder schottischen Dialekt hin, und der Kopist kannte sich bei einigen Tanzarten nicht aus. (Air oder Corant, 33 und Air oder Alman, 47). Das erste betitelte Stück (**13**) führt eine komplett betitelte französische Suite ein: *Prelude – Allemande – Courante – Sarabande* (mit *Variation*).

Alle Anmerkungen vom Herausgeber stehen in eckigen Klammern [ ]. Dart identifizierte **3** als «corant» und **4** als «Sarabande», obwohl sie *contrafacta* zu sein scheinen;

---

4 Diese Identifikation wurde von Peter Holman gegeben.
5 Siehe Watkins Shaw *The Succession of Organists*, Oxford (1999), S. 77.
6 Diese Information kommt von François-Pierre Goy.
7 Siehe C. Bailey, 'Préludes non mesurés en Angleterre' in *Revue de musicologie* 87 Nr. 2 (2001), S. 289.

5 könnte als andere Abart gesehen werden, mit gleichbleibender Harmonie, und alle drei sind didaktische Beispiele. Von *Melothesia* stammt die Idee, **7** als «Jig-Almaine» zu bezeichnen (das ganze Stück könnte in zusammengesetztem Dreiertakt gespielt werden; siehe unten). In Frankreich waren Gigues oft nicht von Allemandes zu unterscheiden (siehe Lautensammlungen wie *La Rhétorique des Dieux*), und in den Bauyn Manuskripten werden zwei Allemandes von J. C. de la Barre *verbatim* wiederholt, während der Titel zu «Gigue» geändert wurde. In England notierte Benjamin Rogers eine Gigue im Almain Rhythmus (Och. 1236, Bl. 41ᵛ–42), und andere Jig-Almains finden sich von Albertus Bryne in Bod. Ms. Mus. Sch. D. 219 und Och. 1177 und bei Moss in *Melothesia*.

Die Sammlung scheint keine Sarabanden mit dem typischen Anfangsschema von drei wiederholten Noten zu enthalten; allerdings scheint **36** trotz des Titels («A little courant») die Anfangsphraseologie und den Stil einer Sarabande aufzuweisen (und melodisch ist sie auch mit dem vorhergehenden Courant verwandt); wahrscheinlich ist das wieder ein Beispiel von fehlerhaftem Kopieren. Die Rondoform von **51** – es könnte ein *Hornpipe* oder *Round O* oder *Jig* sein (wie *Melothesia* Nr. 16) – ist ungewöhnlich, da sie aus vier Teilen besteht, deren erster um eine Oktave höher im dritten Teil wiederholt wird.

Keiner der Bibelverse, die **57** und **58** einleiten, dürfte *verbatim* von den gängigen Alttestamentübersetzungen stammen (Tyndale, Coverdale, Common Prayer 1599, Breeches Bible 1603), kommen jedoch der Reims Douai Übersetzung am nächsten, die 1609 gedruckt wurde. Auch ist es seltsam, dass ein Komponist für Tasteninstrumente sich nicht lieber an die Referenz «Virginalien und Orgeln» von den Übersetzungen 1599 und 1603 hält als an «Saiteninstrumente und Orgeln».

Der Nachweis, dass die Sammlung nach Plan kopiert wurde, ist aus der Korrektur in den Titeln von **44** und **45** ersichtlich («Ein kurzer *Eare* als Präludium vor dem anderen *Eare* gespielt zu werden»), aus den zwei vollständigen Suiten **13–16b** und **17–21** (obwohl nicht so betitelt)

und anderer, weniger weitschweifiger Gruppierung nach Tonart, obwohl später hinzugefügte Tänze manchmal die geplante Abfolge unterbrechen. Die Identifikation von Gruppierungen als Suiten im Inhaltsverzeichnis dieser Ausgabe stammt vom Herausgeber. Es mag zwar zu optimistisch klingen, hat aber zwei Vorteile:

1. absichtliche Folgen in einfacher Tonalität aufzuzeigen und diese von progressiven, didaktischen Beispielen (**1** und **2**, **3–5**) sowie von solchen in zufälligen Tonfolgen zu unterscheiden;

2. den Spieler zu ermutigen, diese Suiten im Anfangsstadium mit Stücken aus anderen Teilen der Sammlung oder vielleicht sogar aus anderen Quellen zu erweitern; Suiten wurden normalerweise nicht von einem einzigen Komponisten geschrieben (Purcells Postumus *Choice Collection* war die erste Ausnahme). H Moll ist die entfernteste Tonart, die hier vorkommt (selten, jedoch von Draghi bevorzugt) und scheint durch eine Folge steigender Tonhöhen hervorgerufen: **44** bis **51** bewegen sich durch A, B, C und D.

Variationen über einen *Basso ostinato* waren in dieser Zeit populär, und La Folia gibt es nur allzuhäufig in Manuskripten des 17. und frühen 18. Jhs. Die vorliegende Sammlung enthält ebenfalls eine Bergamaske, ebenso Entwürfe und Basslinien, die uns annehmen lassen, dass solche Grundmuster für den Unterricht bestimmt waren (siehe Anhang I).

Alle Sätze mit Variationen wurden vom Kopisten B geschrieben, wobei Courants mehr als alle anderen Tanzformen *doubles* aufweisen. Sicher waren die Variationen wegen des Umblätterns nicht für *alternatim*-Spielen bestimmt; allerdings sind die Variationen in **9** und **9b**, wie sie in Och. 1177 erhalten sind, eingeschoben, und wo immer möglich, werden in dieser Ausgabe solche Paare am Anfang zusammen gruppiert, um dem modernen Musiker eine Wahl zu geben.

Es kann sein, dass außer der Ouvertüre zwei Allemandes für Clavichord, Lullys Gavotte (**23**) und andere Stücke Bearbeitungen sind. Diejenigen mit laufenden Terzen und Sexten (z.B. **27**, **34**, **35b**) oder mit Imitation

zwischen den inneren Stimmen deuten auf Originale für Instrumentengruppen, wie diejenigen mit besonders hohen oder tiefen Lagen.

Einige der kurzen Kritzeleien und Übungen in dieser Unterrichtssammlung sind vielleicht mit den Stücken verwandt, denen sie folgen; sie stammen alle vom Kopisten B (oder einem Schüler) und sind in Anhang I wiedergegeben. Die bezifferten Bässe auf Seite 33 und 64 (ebenfalls in Anhang I) haben die gleiche Folge nur in einer anderen Notation.

Die Musik ist überall auf einem sechs-linigen Notensystem niedergeschrieben, in C, G, und F-Schlüsseln; G4 wird einmal in **55**, Takt 250 benützt (möglicherweise wegen einer Korrektur um eine Terz), und Musik für jede Hand bleibt auf ihren eigenen Notenlinien, wie im 17. Jh. üblich. Balken und Bindungen werden wie im Original wiedergegeben. Manchmal ist eine Bindung das Ergebnis einer Zeilentrennung, aber meistens, wie Playford in *Musicks Hand-maid* bemerkt, «viele Achteln und Sechzehnteln sind mit einem Strich durch die Noten zusammengebunden; aber es ist nur für Bequemlichkeit gemacht und ändert nichts an dem Rhythmus». In **57** und **58** ist eine Bindung doppelt, und ein einziger Legatobogen über mehr als zwei Noten wie in **55** und **43**, Takt 17, bedeutet wahrscheinlich eine durchgehende Bindung. In dieser Ausgabe werden solche Nuancen beibehalten, da gebundene Noten im allgemeinen je nach Instrumententyp wiederholt werden können. Ähnlich kann die verschiedene Bindung von Notengruppen durch Balken Phrasierung, Fingersatz und Artikulation verdeutlichen.

Vorzeichen und Tonartvorzeichen werden oft freizügig und modal gehandhabt. Das Präludium der D Moll Suite (**13–16b**) kommt mit einem ♭, der Rest ohne Tonartvorzeichen, wogegen C Moll (**42**, **43**) durch zwei ♭ bezeichnet ist. Auflösungszeichen werden nicht gebraucht und es wird angenommen, dass Vorzeichen normalerweise (aber nicht immer) nur für eine Note gelten. Herausgeberinterventionen, die in [ ] stehen, wollen hier so wenig wie möglich eingreifen; ein Spieler kann selbstverständlich andere Entscheidungen treffen.

Wie das Repertoire zeigen auch die Verzierungen eine Mischung aus neuem französischen und anglo-holländischen Stil. Fünf allgemeingängige Symbole werden bei Locke 1673 aufgelistet, andere kann man bei Prencourt, Blakeston (Add. 17853, datiert 1694), Robert Carr (1684) und Purcell gemeinsam mit deren Vorschlägen zur Realisierung finden.

Tabelle von Verzierungen

In französischer Musik zeigte allerdings ein ⌣ einen Triller oder *tremblement* an, und *port de voix*, meistens als ⌐ oder ⌐ gezeigt, bedeutete obere oder untere Appoggiaturen; das einfache *pincé* ⌐ = ⌐ gab es im 17. Jh. in England nicht; Purcell bemerkte «man trillert immer von der oberen Note und schlägt von der unteren oder einer halben darunter».

Die Plazierung von doppelschlägigen Verzierungen ist verschieden, manchmal über der Note, manchmal durch den Hals; solche Unterschiede sind in der vorliegenden Ausgabe erhalten.[8] Es ist fraglich, ob zwischen einem Doppelschlag und einem französischen Triller innerhalb desselben Stücks (**46**) oder sogar auf derselben Note (**53**, Takt 4) ein Unterschied besteht; letzteres könnte eine Alternative oder ein Umdenken sein wie auch die Kombi-

8 Siehe John Harley 'Ornaments in English Keyboard Music of the Seventeenth and Eighteenth Centuries', *Music Review* 31 (1970), S. 178–184.

nation von «chute» plus Triller in **16**, Takt 11. Der Doppelschlag wird oft dort verwendet, wo eine französische Quelle ein *pincé* haben würde, und eine derartige Verzierung impliziert sicher eine untere Wechselnote, wenn mit dem «4». (in **52**) Finger gespielt.

In einigen Stücken werden gemischte Verzierungen verwendet: Vorschlag von oben und Triller z.B. in **11**, Takt 7 und 20, sowie **51**, Takt 16 und **52**, Takt 10; die gebundene Note vor einem doppelschlägigen Triller in **18** und **22** verhindert wahrscheinlich die normale Wiederholung der oberen Note.

Die Bezeichnung für ein Arpeggio oder eine «Batterie» – die in den meisten englischen Ausgaben als ein Arpeggio nach oben interpretiert wird – wurde vielleicht auch in französischer Manier ausgeführt, mit Durchgangsnoten, wie von D'Anglebert (1689) vorgeschlagen:

oder sogar als wiederholtes Arpeggio, wie Prencourt meint:

Letzteres könnte für **58**, Takt 27 und weiterhin gelten.

Der Schleifer ist in **53** voll ausgeschrieben und das einzige Auftreten einer Verzierung eines Einzelschlags (**58**, Takt 158) ist wahrscheinlich ein Fehler (wie in Elizabeth Rogers' Virginal-Buch), oder aber ein Anzeichen eines weiteren Schleifers.

Gleichzeitige Verzierungen in l.H. und r.H. gibt es in **49**, Takt 16, **55**, Takt 56, **42** Takt 10, 17, 21, 24, **46**, Takt 13, und in **50**, Takt 20 wird die Verzierung zweimal auf derselben Note markiert. Doppelte Verzierungen – doppelter Schlag und französischer Triller – gibt es in **53**, Takt 4, und mehrere Takte in **42** gebrauchen zwei unterschiedliche Triller gleichzeitig. Triller werden in **58** voll ausgeschrieben wie im Stil früherer Virginalien; von den linkshändigen Trillern schrieb Roger North, «Es ist gebräuchlich unter Organisten, statt die Verzierung, die *beat-up* [d.h. Vorschlag von unten] genannt wird auf den unteren Tasten zwei Töne gleichzeitig, eine kleine Sekunde getrennt, zu

halten; es bewirkt das gleiche mit einem besseren Effekt».

In **51** und anderswo scheint der Unterschied zwischen Vorschlag von unten und Vorschlag von oben manchmal verwischt; die letzten Takte von **51** sollten sicherlich eine Verzierung von unten und nicht von oben haben. Die ∧ Verzierung in **13**, Takt 3 kann nicht identifiziert werden, obwohl wahrscheinlich ein Vorschlag von unten und Vorschlag von oben, eine Art von Doppelschlag, ausgeführt werden soll; sie taucht nur noch einmal bei Hotteterre auf, wo sie ein «coulement» oder eine obere Appoggiatur bedeutet. Chromatische Tonmodulation wird nie angedeutet, da angenommen wird, dass alle Verzierungen in der vorherrschenden Tonart stattfinden (z.B. der Triller in **28**, Takt 62 steht mit einem As).

Ein Doppeltakt in einem Tanzsatz wird hier als Wiederholungszeichen interpretiert (Purcell erklärt es «bedeutet man muss diesen Teil nochmals spielen»). In Stücken, die mehr als zwei Teile aufweisen (wie Bergamasken und Folia Varianten), sind solche Wiederholungen ad libitum; **49** ist im Gegensatz zu den meisten Airs in vier Teile geteilt, jedoch nur zwei davon implizieren Wiederholungen. Eine *petite reprise* wird in **52** angedeutet (z.B. beide Teile ganz wiederholt *und* die *petite reprise*) und in **33** ausgeschrieben. Diese Formel kann in anderen Tanzsätzen je nach Laune gebraucht werden.

Die Originalnotation der letzten Takte in zweiteiligen Stücken ist erhalten, muss aber manchmal für Auftakte adaptiert oder für einen besseren Übergang geändert werden; Lösungen enthalten Unterlassung einer zweiten Verknüpfung (**3**, l.H., Takt 16), Weglassen einer Note, die mit dem Auftakt das erste Mal in Konflikt geraten würde (**1**, l.H., Takt 4) oder Hinzufügen eines zusätzlichen Kadenztaktes (wie der Vergleich der Originaltexte von **9** und **9b** zeigt). Notenwerte der Akkorde in Kadenztakten sind manchmal zufällig und können zwischen r.H. und l.H. je nach dem voraussichtlichen Auftakt variieren; aber nachdem die Absicht immer klar ist, wurden sie vom Herausgeber nicht verändert. Sehr selten sind erste und Wiederholungstakte wirklich präzise notiert: siehe **14**, Takt 8 und 16.

Das konventionelle, linkshändige Kadenzmuster wie in **1**, Takt 4 wird manchmal mit der niedrigsten Note gehalten notiert (siehe **2**), was eine andere Überlegato-Interpretation sein könnte. Gewöhnlich können Kadenzakkorde, die ein Arpeggio haben, mit Bindungen verbessert werden, und in all den Stücken mit *brisure* wäre ein Überlegato angebracht. Eine Alternativquelle für **9** (Och. 1177) gibt z.B. Bindungen (tenuto anzeigend) über fast die ganzen Achtelgruppen, andere Versionen von **6** weisen eine dichter ausgefüllte linke Hand auf, und Spieler können sie je nach Geschmack umarbeiten. Einfügungen vom Herausgeber werden nur dann gemacht, wenn Zweideutigkeit oder ein unwillkommener harmonischer Bruch auftreten.

Mehr als die Hälfte der Stücke in diesem Manuskript hat methodische Fingersätze und daher gehört es zu den instruktivsten Quellen des 17. Jhs. für englische Technik. Allerdings ist das gebrauchte System mit × (Daumen)–1–2–3–4 typischer für italienische als englische oder französische Notation; es wird auch von keinem anderen Engländer außer Prencourt, mit Daumen–1–2–3–4, benützt. (Roger North, *Plaine & Easie Rules* ca. 1700) Die Bezifferung ist modernisiert und gibt – mit gewissen Einschränkungen – wichtige Informationen über Anschlag, Artikulation, Verzierung, Tempo und Akkorde; manchmal wurden Fingersätze *vor* den Innenstimmen niedergeschrieben (siehe **2b**, Takt 4 und 8) oder in anderen Stücken vor einer Verzierung (**36b**); in einigen Fällen sind sie völlig unmöglich (**35b**, Takt 16, l.H., siehe Revisionsbericht). Trotzdem können einige Allgemeinregeln abgeleitet werden: Wiederholung einer Note geschieht mit Fingerwechsel; Fingerwechsel auf einer gehaltenen Note wird erwartet (**1b**, Takt 8); auf einer kurzen Taste wird häufig der Daumen gebraucht (**26b**, r.H. Takt 19 und 25), ebenso für lange Folgen von Innenstimmen (**45b**, Takt 10–11); in Folgen von Sechsten und Terzen (**35b**) wird ein relativ «moderner» Fingersatz benützt, um den Aussenstimmen Legato zu geben, andrerseits werden wieder lange Folgen mit demselben Finger gehalten zugelassen.

Nur ein Stück in der Sammlung hat eine Tempobezeichnung («Schnell» für **5**), aber für viele Tänze würde das Taktzeichen eine Tempobezeichnung bedeuten; Purcells *Choice Collection of Lessons* (1696) erklärt die drei Bezeichnungen – **c**, **₵**, **Ø** – so: «Das erste ist ein sehr langsamer Satz, das nächste ein bisschen schneller, und das letzte frisch und luftig, und alle haben sie die Dauer einer ganzen Note, die so lange gehalten werden soll, dass man gemächlich vier zählen kann, wenn man eins, zwei, drei, vier sagt». Andere zeitgenössische Autoren stimmen überein, dass **Ø** «frisch und luftig» und «so schnell wie die regelmässige Bewegung einer Uhr bedeutet» (d.h. ♩ = MM 120).

Playford notierte in 1694 für den Dreiertakt $\frac{3}{2}$ als das langsamste, **3** oder **3₁** als schneller und $\frac{3}{8}$ als «noch einmal so schnell». Ein weiterer Unterschied wird 1696 in der *Choice Collection* aufgeführt, wobei **3₁** «drei Vierteln im Takt hat, und sie sollen langsam gespielt werden», während **3** «die gleichen wie die vorigen hat aber schneller gespielt». Der Dreiertakt war in der Sarabande am langsamsten; diese war ursprünglich ein schneller Tanz, aber gegen Ende des 17. Jhs. ein «sanfter leidenschaftlicher Satz immer im langsamen Dreiertakt gesetzt» nach Dean Aldrichs Beschreibung. (Och. MS 1187, ca. 1695). Der Dreiertaktteil der Farmer-Ouvertüre (**28**, Takt 22) ist überraschenderweise ebenfalls als «langsame Zeit» in der originalen Version für Instrumentengruppen angeführt.

In den Sätzen mit Variationen bedeutet die Ausschmückung des *double* ein moderates Tempo, besonders bei Almands. Der französische Titel Allemande (acht Stücke sind so benannt und eine «Eare or Allemande») impliziert keinen Tempounterschied zur einfachen englischen Alemand (**27**). Die beiden letzten Orgelsoli sollten vielleicht verschiedene Tempi aus Kontrastgründen erhalten, vielleicht sogar *senza misura* in der Manier einer italienischen Toccata.

Die Einstufung von punktierten Rhythmen war ein wichtiger Aspekt des Aufführungsstils, eintweder mit «Doppelpunktierung» (moderner Ausdruck) oder *notes inégales*, ebenso wie die Verkürzungen des Auftakts und der Noten nach Pausen. Das stimmt allerdings nicht immer

wie **27** zeigt, wo das gleichmäßig punktierte Muster, das nach Pausen impliziert ist, *nicht* angewendet wird, auch wenn es hätte notiert werden können (Takt 20). Die ungewöhnliche rhythmische Verschiedenartigkeit von **7** [Jigg-Almaine] lässt auf eine Assimilation der Triolen oder sogar eine Adaption des Metrums vom ganzen Stück zu einem zusammengesetzten Takt schließen. Ein Modell dafür liefern zwei unterschiedliche, zeitgenössische Notationen für eine Froberger Gigue:

Gigue (Suite VII). Froberger's authograph

Gigue (Suite XXIII). Bauyn MS

Analog, würde der Anfang von **7** so gespielt:

Playford listet die für ein solches Repertoire richtigen Instrumente auf: «Das *Virginal* wird mit einem einzelnen Chor gespannt; das *Cembalo* mit zwei oder mehr und es ist voller und lauter; die *Orgel* hat ein Gestell, das unterschiedliche Gruppen oder Register von Pfeifen beherbergen kann». Er zeigt ein kurzoktaviges Tasteninstrument mit der tiefsten Note C, aber macht darauf aufmerksam, dass der Umfang von «29 Tasten nach dem alten Standard» war und «dass seit kurzer Zeit obere und untere Noten dazugekommen sind». Die vorliegende Sammlung benützt das tiefste G einmal (**22**) und das tiefste A einige Male (**14**, **16**, **16b**, **53**); in *Melothesia* gibt es ein tiefes H (von Preston benützt), tiefes A (Preston Moss, Thatcher, Locke) und das tiefste G (Diessner), was die Vorlieben verschiedener Komponisten für gewisse Umfänge anzeigen könnte. Die beiden «Voluntaries» [Orgelsoli vor, bei und nach dem anglikanischen Gottesdienst] (**57, 58**) sind trotz ihrer Ähnlichkeit zu zeitgenössischen Stücken nicht für geteilte Register geschrieben (tiefe und hohe Teile setzen sich über mögliche Teilungen eines Registers hinweg); mit einigen Ausnahmen werden Handzusammenstöße vermieden, und das weist auf ein einmanualiges Instrument hin.

Nach Grassineaus Wörterbuch von 1740 «kann das Chlarichord oder Manichord auf grössere Entfernung nicht gehört werden; daher wird es von einigen das stumme Spinett genannt». Von französischen Titelseiten (Attaingnant's *Quatorze Gaillardes... en la tabulature du jeu d'Orgues Espinettes Manicordions ... 1531) sowie aus italienischen Sammlungen (Gardano's *Intabolatura nova ... da sonare per arpichordi, Claviciembali, Spinette, & Manachordi ... 1551) war die Bezeichnung international seit über einem Jahrhundert bekannt. Die beiden Allemandes «fitt (= arrangiert) for the Manichorde» sind allerdings die einzigen Stücke englischen Ursprungs, die dieses Instrument verlangen. Die Vermutung, dass die Sammlung für Clavichordmusik bestimmt sei wird durch eine einzige, notierte dynamische Veränderung, die «eccho»-Bezeichnung in **40**, unterstützt. Diese Art von Anweisung ist in der englischen Tastenmusik selten (ein Satz von John Roberts (Almain) in Drexel 5611 weist eine Passage mit der Anweisung «softly» auf), aber die Instruktion hier (Takt 25–26) schließt einen Wechsel der Tastatur aus, wenn die Stimmen gespielt werden sollen wie sie niedergeschrieben sind, angenommen, dass «eccho» sich auf beide Systeme bezieht; ein Clavichord wäre das einzige Instrument, das diese Nuance buchstäblich durchführen kann.

Danksagung

Für ihre vielseitige Hilfe bei der Herstellung der vorliegenden Ausgabe sei Robert Rawson, Curtis Lasell, Prof. Eamon Duffy, Robert Thompson, der verstorbene Robert Spencer, Peter Holman, Bruce Gustafson, François-Pierre Goy, Derek Adlam, Heather Jarman, David Chung und Per Hartmann besonderer Dank ausgesprochen.

Bibliographie

Candace Bailey: *English Keyboard Music c.1625–1680* (PhD diss.: Duke University, 1989)

John Caldwell: *English Keyboard Music before the Nineteenth Century* (Blackwell, Oxford, 1973)

Barry Cooper: *English Solo Keyboard Music of the Middle and Late Baroque* (Garland, New York, 1989)

Bruce Gustafson and R. Peter Wolf, eds: *Harpsichord Music Associated with the Name of La Barre* (Broude Trust, New York, 1999).

John Harley: *British Harpsichord Music* (Scolar Press, Aldershot, 1992–4)

J. Brian Hodge: *English Harpsichord Repertoire, 1660–1714.* (PhD diss.: University of Manchester, 1989)

Matthew Locke (ed. Hogwood): *Melothesia* (Oxford University Press, 1987)

Roger North (ed. Wilson): *On Music; Being a Selection from his Essays, Written during the Years ca. 1695–1728* (Novello, London, 1959)

Christopher Hogwood
Cambridge, Juni 2003
hogwood@hogwood.org
Übersetzung Burgi Hartmann

1 · [Almand]

1b · [Variation]

HH 11 070

Edited by Christopher Hogwood
© Copyright 2003 by Edition HH Ltd
Printed in England

2

2 · [Almand]

2b · [Variation]

3 · [Air]

4 · [Air]

4

5 · [Jigg] Fast

6 · [Almand]

7 · [Jig-Almand]

8 · [Almand] [? John Roberts]

9 · [Corant] [? John Roberts]

9b · [Variation] [? John Roberts]

10 · [Corant] [La Barre]

10b · [Variation] [La Barre]

11 · [Jigg]

11b · [Variation]

12 · [Corant]

12b · [Variation]

13 · Prelude

12

14 · Allemande

15 · Courante

16 · Sarabande

16b · [Variation]

17 · [Prelude]

18 · [Almand]

19 · [Corant]

20 · [Saraband]

16

20b · [Variation]

21 · [Bergamask]

HH 11 070

22 · [Air]

23 · [Gavotte] [Lully]

24 · [Sarabande]

25 · [Courant]

26 · [Sarabande]

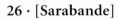

26b · Variation

27 · Almand

28 · An Overture, wch the Organist of Chichister desired to have set [Thomas Farmer]

26

29 · An Allemande

30 · A Courante

30b · A Variation

31 · An Allemande

28

32 · A french Eare

32b · A Variation

Facsimile 1: folio 104, bars 1–11 of the first 'Allemande fitt for the Manicorde' (**42**, p. 37)

33 · An Eare or a Courante

34 · An Allemande

35 · A Courante

35b · A Variation

36 · A litle courant [? Sarabande]

36b · A Variation

37 · An Allemande

38 · A Courante [La Barre]

38b · A Variation [La Barre]

39 · An Allemande

39b · A Variation

40 · A Courant

41 · A Courante

42 · An Allemande fitt for the Manicorde

43 · An Allemande fitt for the Manicorde

44 · A short Eare in way of a Prelude, to be play'd before the other Eare

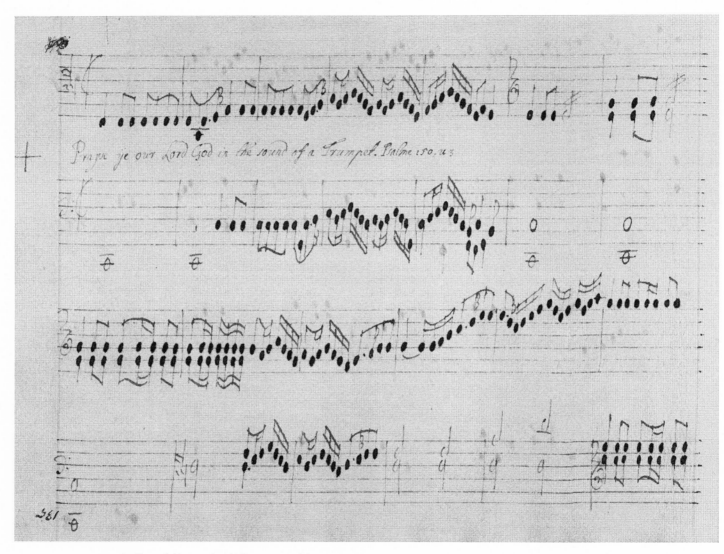

Facsimile 2: folio 135 (rev), bars 1–13 of 'Prayse ye our Lord God in the sound of a Trumpet' (**58**, p. 61)

45 · An Eare

45b · A Variation

46 · A Courante

47 · An Eare or Allemande

48 · An Eare

44

49 · An Eare

50 · Corrantt

HH 11 070

51 · [Hornpipe]

52 · [Sarabande]

[dal 𝄋]

53 · Jigg

54 · [Trumpet Air]

[Variation]

55 · [Variations on 'La Folia']

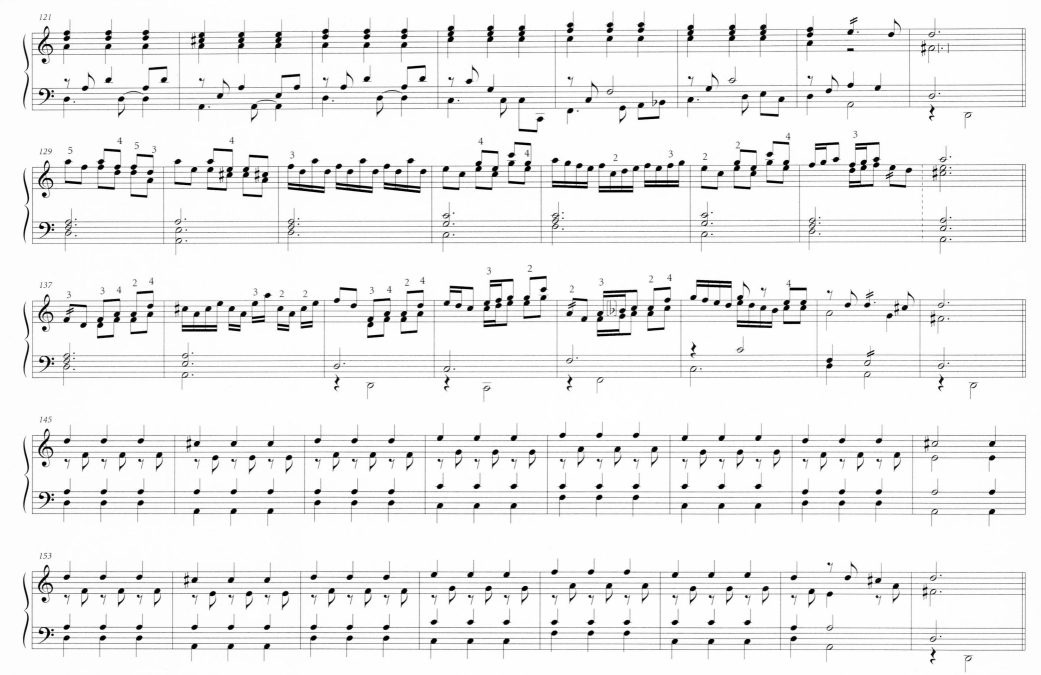

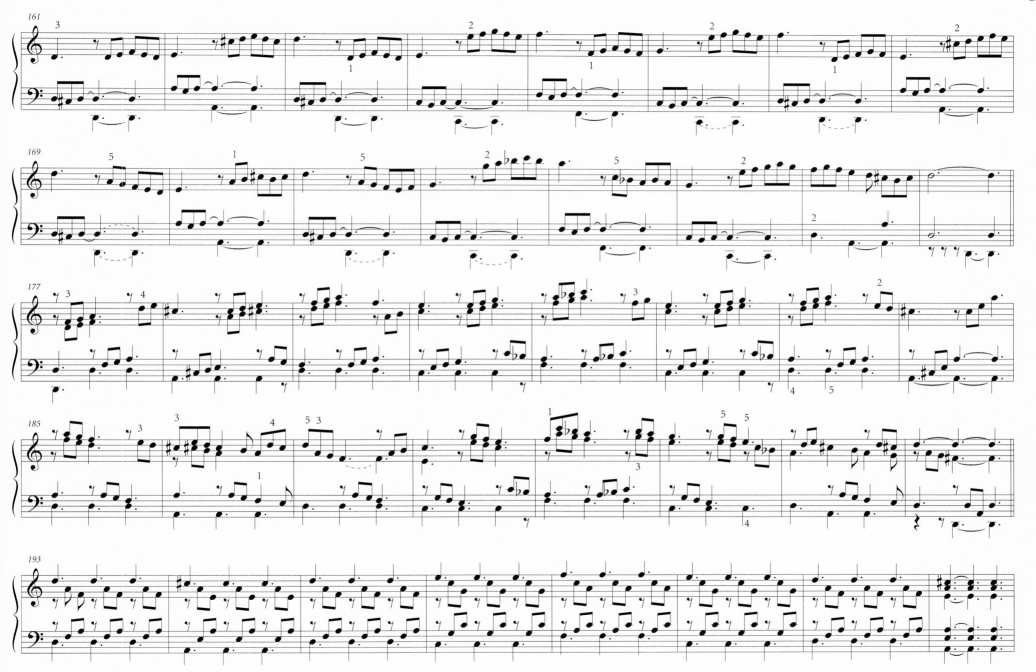

Laus Deo

56 · [Variations on a Ground]

57 · **Prayse ye our Lord God on strings and Organs.** Psalme 150, v. 4

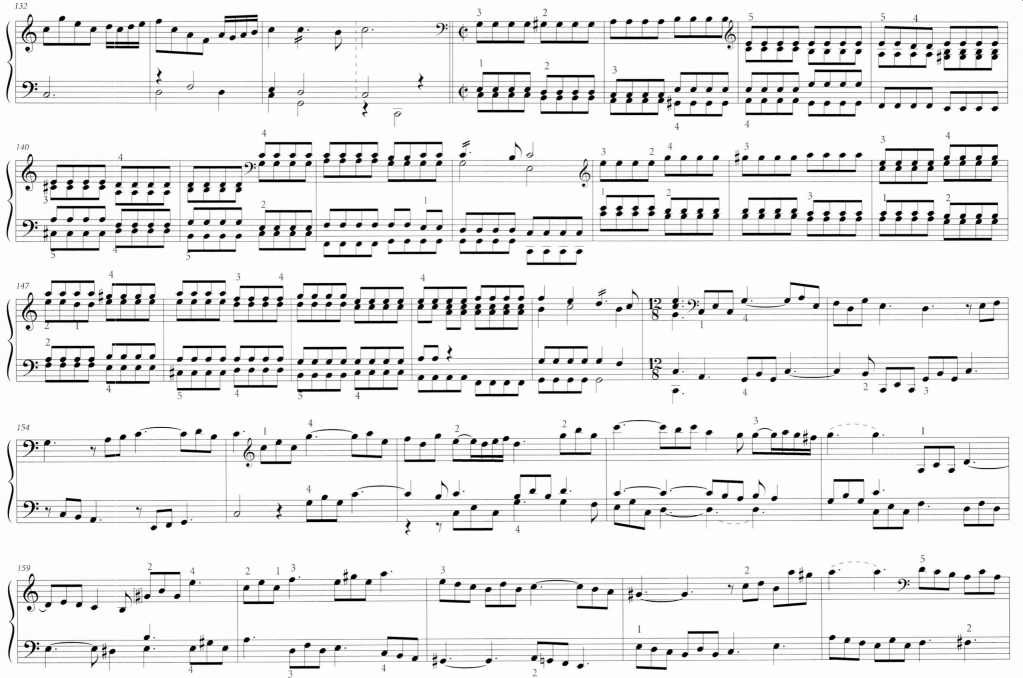

58 · **Prayse ye our Lord God in the sound of a Trumpet.** Psalme 150, v. 3

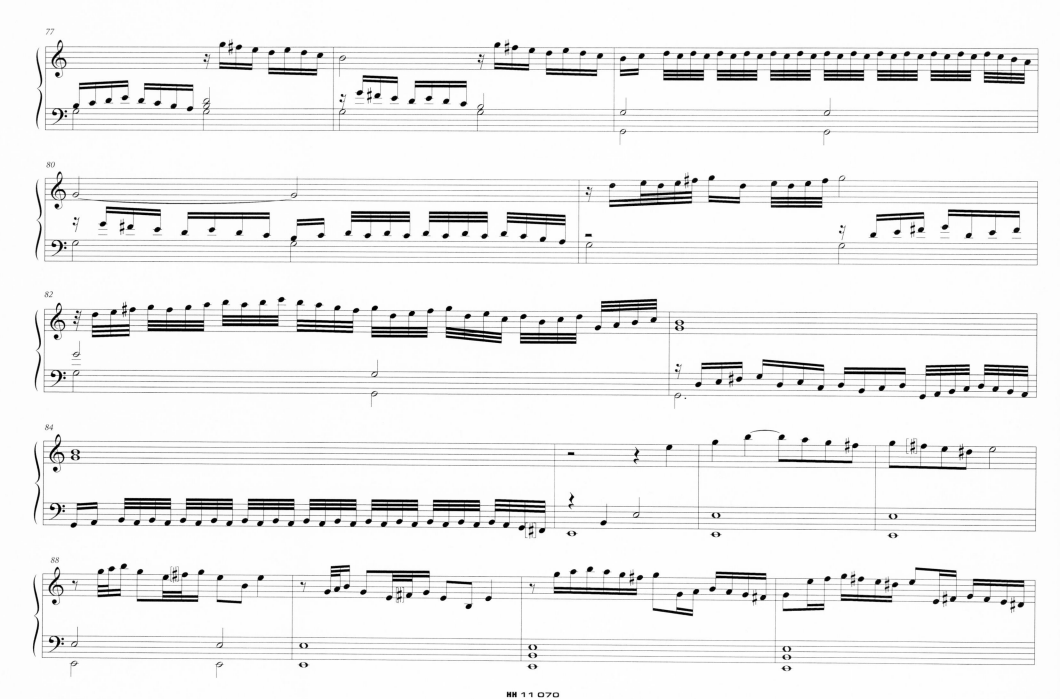

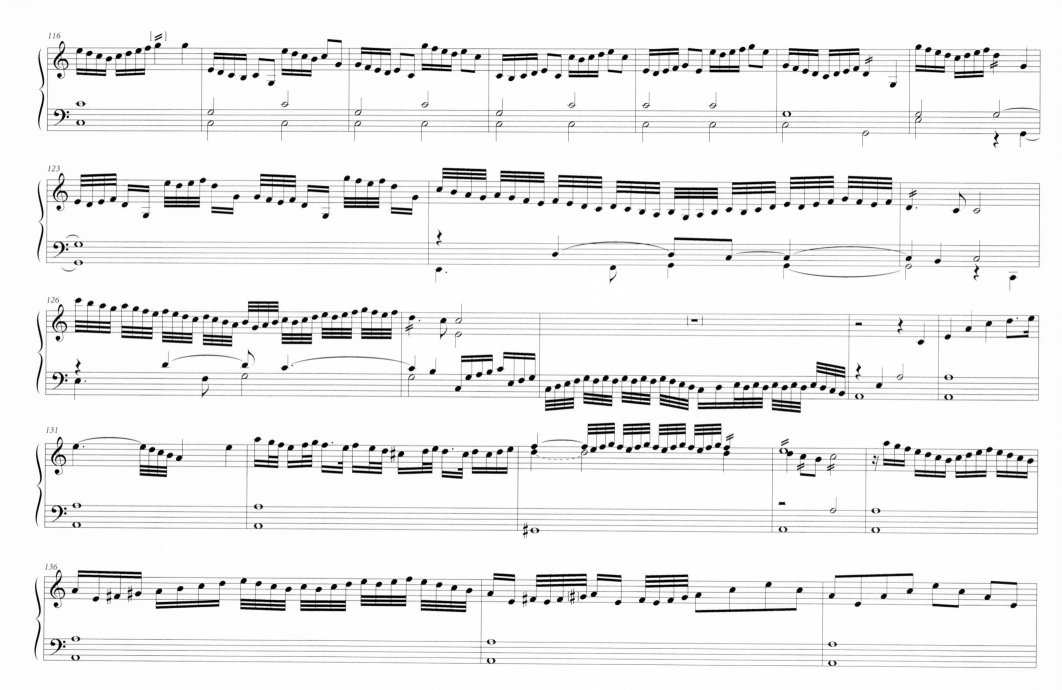

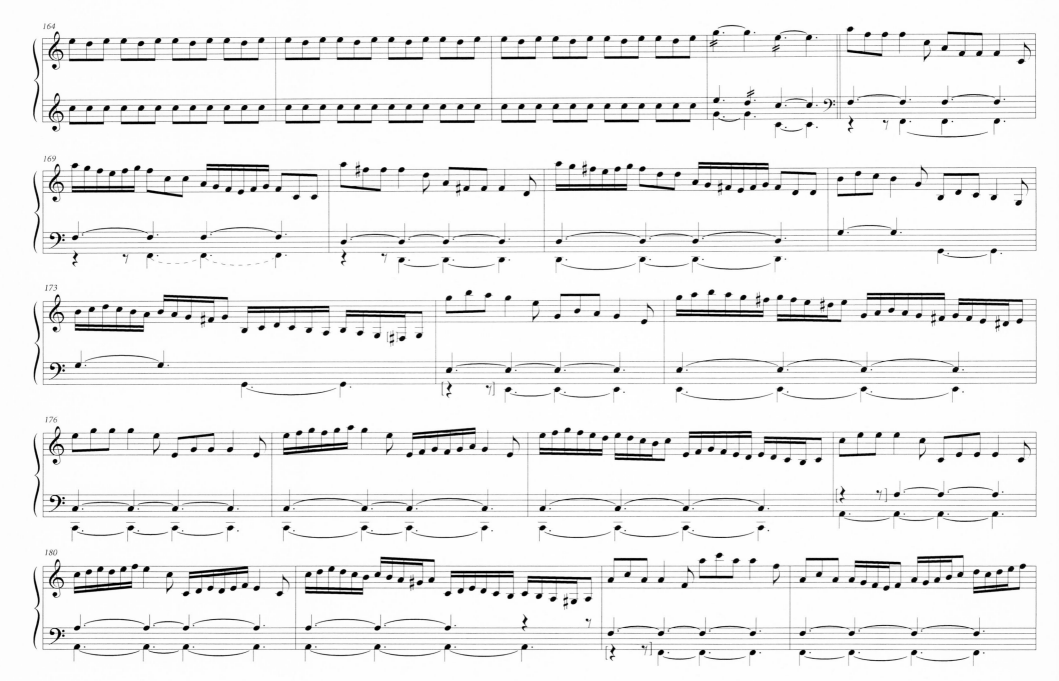

thanks to Almighty God and to the Blessed Virgin Mary mother of God

HH 11 070

Appendix I

Example 1: p. 13 following **8**

Example 2: p. 33 following **17**

Example 3: p. 35 following **18**

Example 4: p. 43 following **22**

Example 5: p. 51 following **25**

Example 6: p. 51 following Example 5

Example 7: p. 64 on blank opening within **28**

Example 8: p. 64 following Example 7

Example 9: p. 175 following **53**

Example 10: p. 173 following **54**

Appendix II · Overture (28) · Thomas Farmer

72

Textual notes / Revisionsbericht

piece	MS page	bar	stave	comment
1	3			
1b	4	1	lh	no time-signature
		6	lh	n. 2: originally D, corrected to F but not erased
2	5	4	rh	n. 5: C dotted
2b	6	4	rh	n. 9: presumably fingered before the alto E was added (also b. 8)
3	7	16	lh	the last three notes to be played first time only
4	8			
5	9			
6	10	15	rh	n. 2: semiquaver, corrected to quaver with additional tail
7	11			at the triplet notation the lh is written as dotted crotchets when there are triplets above
		6	lh	second half a third lower
		7	lh	page damaged, and bass missing on beat 1
8	12–13	1	rh	n. 1: fingered 3, changed to 4
		7	lh	bass nn. 2–3 missing (page torn)
		10	lh	n. 3: a third lower
9	14–15	28	rh	the editorial natural is found in the Variation (9b) and in Och. 1177
9b	16–17	7	rh	n. 5: fingering unclear
		16	lh	tenor n. 1 notated as a minim (also b. 33)
10	18	1	rh	n. 1: finger changed from × to 1 (i.e. 1 to 2)
		3–5	rh	the fingering here ('1') is sufficiently slanted to possibly be intended as backfalls
10b	19			
11	20	7, 20	rh	compound ornaments
11b	21	7	lh	n. 1 tailed in both directions; but minim rest in bass
		12		last beat missing (page cropped)
		22	lh	tenor part specifically altered to read minim B flat, crotchet C
		24		final double bar-line missing (page cropped)
12	22			
12b	23			
13	24–25			
14	26–27	6	lh	first bass note fingering 3 (=4) changed to 4 (=5)
		7	lh	bass n. 1: A deleted
15	28–29	15	rh	bottom note of chord, no dot
		24	rh	n. 1; '3' deleted and '1' substituted
16	30	5	lh	n. 1 marked with an unclear sign that might be ornament or fingering ('×' = 1)
16b	31	1	rh	t.s. ¢ and 3 in rh stave only
		16	lh	bass note: C and F above; final double bar missing
17	32–33			
18	34–35		lh	no time-signature
		1	rh	chord: E,G with one dot only
		5	lh	n. 3: fingering unclear (maybe erased with previous E?)
		11	lh	n. 1: the A may be a miscopying, and could be omitted
		15	rh	n. 6: fingered both '1' and '2'
19	36–37			
20	38	2	lh	n. 1: fingering given is '×' (= 1); probably 5 is intended
		16	lh	lacking final bar-line
20b	39			
21	40–41	0		ϕ in l.h. margin (possibly implying double time)
		4		double-barlines here and throughout could imply repeats, as in bipart-ite dances
22	42–43			
23	44–45	5		triple barline
		10	lh	n. 2: a third higher in MS
		11	lh	bass n. 4 displaced before n. 3
		13	lh	tenor n. 2 lacking tail; tenor n. 3 is a crotchet rest
		14	lh	bass n. 1: G
24	48–49			this untitled dance is probably a Sarabande, since, prior to 23 being copied, there were sufficient blank pages left for two dances to precede it
25	50–51	1	rh	nn. 3 and 4 are possibly reversed (read C, B)
		8	lh	bass n. 3: originally '×' changed to '4'
26	52–53	5	lh	first note A
		29	lh	the fingering suggests that F is intended, though D might be preferred
26b	54–55			
27	56–58	1	lh	n. 3: G
		9	rh	n. 2; F♯
		13	rh	alto thus, but cf. rhythm in bar 26
		15	rh	rhythm thus on beat 3, but possibly three semiquavers are intended (as bars 16, 17)
		26	rh	alto figure possibly intended to be as bar 13
28	60–63, 68	11	rh	n. 2 originally flat, altered to sharp (= natural)
		17	lh	last note thus, but E natural might be preferred

	21, 21a			first- and second-time indications editorial
	22			the consort version is marked 'slow time' here
	28–29		lh	a third lower
	61		lh	bass n. 2 without repeated flat, so A natural is also possible
	77		lh	bass n. 2 partially erased
	78a			second time: rh chord semibreve
29	68–69	2		C doubled thus in both hands on beat 2
30	70–71			the only Courante in this MS written in minims
		7–8		cadential corona over two bars, possibly to indicate the elongated harmony (as e.g. in **35**); similar slurs are found over bars 21–2, without dots. It is unlikely they can be intended as first- and second-time indications, unless the sequence of the bars is reversed and the second bar used for first-time
		21–2		ties, no dots but possibly first/second time bars?
30b	72–73	0	rh	time-signature: ¢ plus ȝ
		8		all dots missing
		21–22		cadential corona over two bars; see note to previous number
31	74–75	8	rh	chord 3: dot missing to B
32	76–77			
32b	78–79	22	rh	last note partially erased; alternatively, ignore the editorial addition and add a crotchet rest before the alto B
33	80–81	20	rh	alto n. 1: E
		24		alto n. 2: D
34	82–83			
35	84–85		lh	time-signature missing
		24–26	rh	chords have been erased on the first beats of these three bars
35b	86–87	16	lh	bass n. 1 fingered '2', but possibly 4 intended
		17	lh	last note thus, but a crotchet would preserve the pattern of the following bars
36	88			
36b	88–89			
37	90–91	20	rh	middle note of chord; no dot
38	92–93	15	rh	alto n. 1: C
		23	rh	sharp deleted before F
38b	94–95	12	rh	dot missing for C sharp
		15	rh	alto n. 1: C
		21	rh	n. 4: sharp for C written one note earlier (on B)
39	96–97	9	lh	nn. 2 and 3 written as dotted crotchet and quaver
39b	98–99			
40	100–101	27	rh	n. 3: crotchet
41	102–103			
42	104–105		rh	time-signature originally 'ȝ', with ¢ written over
		24	lh	the ornament is ambiguous; either over D or the following C
43	106–107			time-signature (¢) before rh stave only
		17	lh	slur in tenor part is possibly derived from a string original; alternatively it may represent a double tie, as in **57** and **58**
		19	lh	fingering '1' ambiguously placed between nn. 1 and 2
44	109			copied out of sequence in the original; in spite of its title it is three bars longer than the air it precedes
		15		after the final bar: 'After this play the former Eare'
45	108–109	1–2	lh	last 4 notes of b. 1 and first note of b. 2 a third lower (but cf. **46b**)
		11–12		between the staves: 'After this play the Variation to it on the other side of the leaf.'
45b	110–111	8	rh	there may be a *lacuna* in the alto beat 2 (end of page), although the ornament may be considered sufficient
		12	rh	n. 1 D, but B preserves the figuration of this section
46	112–113			
47	114–115	10	rh	MS gives alto D in place of rest for beat 1
48	116			
49	117	4		the double bars after bars 4 and 12 would not seem to indicate repeats?
		11	lh	bass n. 1: E
		16		at end (between staves): *Deo Gratias et Maria*
	(*reversed pagination*)			
50	181	17	rh	nn. 2–4: G F E
		19	rh	nn. 2–4: A G E
		20	rh	n.1: ornament written both above the note, and through the tail
		23–24		final bar cropped in MS
51	180–179	3	rh	n. 1: fingering '×' (=1) changed to '2' (=3)
		4		this unusual dissonance is repeated in bars 8 and 12
		16		a repeat of the opening section would preserve the form of a rondeau implied here
52	178–177	21	rh	two segno signs, above and below n. 1, both in rh stave
53	176–175			Note unusual form of 6 bars + 5 bars in each section (possibly the final bars of each half are to be doubled in length)
		4	rh	'doubled' ornament thus, possibly meaning trill with termination.
		17	rh	'×' above stave, probably not a fingering

54	174–173			in the manner of a 'Trumpet Air', and including a variation (possibly a didactic demonstration of imitation)
55	172–150	8		double bar here and throughout, not indicating repeat
		64		F included in both rh and lh
		118		one bar deleted (bass an octave lower than intended)
		142	rh	fingering possibly intended for a note now deleted
		224		final flourish, as if end of piece
		258	rh	change of clef (G4) for one bar to correct miscopying a third higher
		266		to maintain the sequence, the slurs here (new page) can be omitted
		281ff	rh	bars of three crotchets altered in this variation from crotchet + minim, also in lh from bar 289
		304		after final barline: *Laus Deo*
56	149–148			
57	147–136	74	rh	the tie is written twice
		103	rh	rh stave missing (MS cropped)
		156–7	lh	MS gives:
		159	rh	nn. 6–8 a third higher
		179	rh	there appears to be an omission in the alto part here
		185		two 'ornaments' ⁓ are written after rather than above the last notes in each hand, and may simply be intended to draw attention to the change of time-signature
		190		the layout of the hands is unusual here, and may imply the use of two manuals
		198	rh	lower note: G
58	135–118	42	lh	n. 13: quaver
		117–19	lh	all Gs altered from Cs (to avoid a hand collision)
		146		the note C is unusually shared between rh and lh
		158	rh	single-stroke ornaments thus (the only such occurrence in this MS)
		196–7	rh	the tie is written twice
		197		the double-bar written in rh stave only
		200	rh	n. 10: no sharp repeated, therefore natural possible
		206		after final barline: *thanks to Almighty God	and to the Blessed Virgin Mary mother of God.*

Appendix I

These ten examples include all the musically relevant additions made to the manuscript; there are additional scribblings and nib exercises of no musical interest. Figured and unfigured basses with their realization account for most of these excerpts. Example 1 is an unusual version of a bass pattern which would normally have E as the sixth note; the version as found here also occurs. Examples 2 and 8 present the same bass in different notation, and Example 7 appears to be the start of a possible realization. Examples 9 and 10 show simple harmonizations of a rising and falling scale very similar to Locke's examples in *Melothesia*. In some cases the copying of the example after a complete piece in the manuscript suggests a possible connection between the two, possibly an explanation of a harmonic sequence or an outline model for an improvised prelude: Example 9, for example, is very similar to bb. 12–16 of the preceding **53**. Example 6 is written in the 'pupil's hand' and does not appear to relate to any piece in the collection. Only three examples suggest a context: Example 3 appears to be a metrical hymn-tune (as yet unidentified), Example 4 the bass to an ensemble dance in E minor, and Example 5 a simple Anglican psalm-chant.

Appendix II

Transcribed from the printed part-books of Thomas Farmer, *A Consort of Musick in four parts containing 33 Lessons beginning with an Overture* (1686), pp. 1–2 in all books; the only surviving copy is in the British Library K.7.c.4 and lacks the viola part-book.